W9-ASQ-811

ELEMENTARY:
THE CARTOONIST DID IT

ELEMENTARY:
THE CARTOONIST DID IT

ROBERT MANKOFF

AVON
PUBLISHERS OF BARD, CAMELOT AND DISCUS BOOKS

ELEMENTARY: THE CARTOONIST DID IT is an original publication of Avon Books. This work has never before appeared in book form.

Of the 111 drawings in this collection, 24 originally appeared in *The New Yorker,* Copyright © 1977, 1978 and 1979 by The New Yorker Magazine, Inc.

AVON BOOKS
A division of
The Hearst Corporation
959 Eighth Avenue
New York, New York 10019

Copyright © 1980 by Robert Mankoff
Published by arrangement with the author
Library of Congress Catalog Card Number: 79-55571
ISBN: 0-380-75318-9

All rights reserved, which includes the right
to reproduce this book or portions thereof in
any form whatsoever. For information address
Avon Books.

First Avon Printing, February, 1980

AVON TRADEMARK REG. U.S. PAT. OFF. AND IN
OTHER COUNTRIES, MARCA REGISTRADA, HECHO EN
U.S.A.

Printed in the U.S.A.

FOR MARCY

MANKOFF

"I'm sorry, but that one was too close to call."

MANKOFF

MANKOFF

When it came to raisins, Mom's motto was "Use your imagination."

"You're wasting your time; I'm asexual."

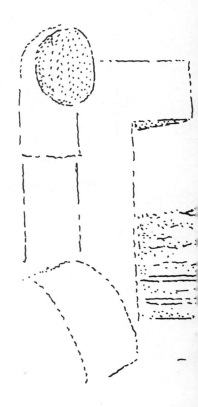

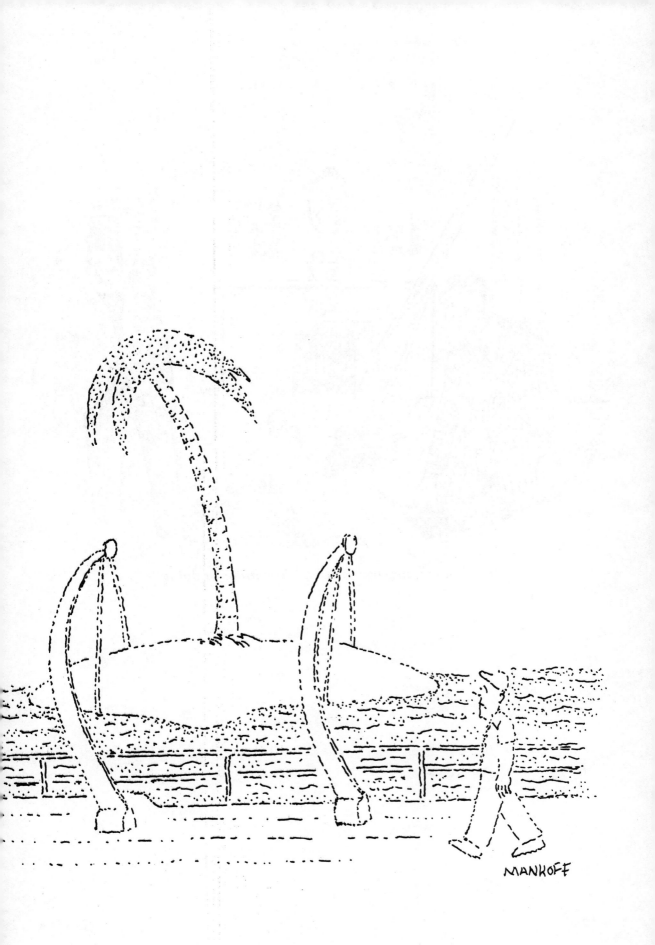

"Elementary, my dear Watson: the cartoonist did it."

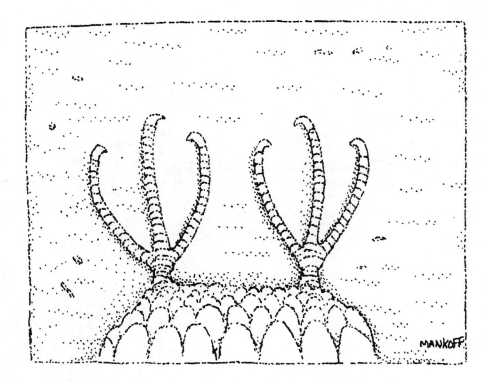

Bird's-Eye View

MANKOFF

LEARNING TO CAST HAND SHADOWS

LESSON # 1

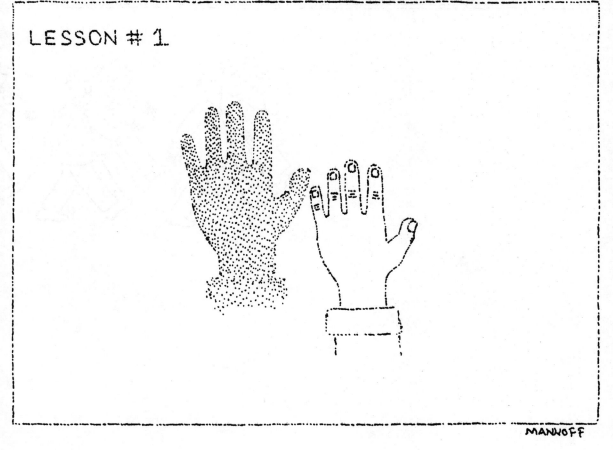

MANNOFF

MANKOFF

"My main fear used to be cats—now it's carcinogens."

MANKOFF

MANKOFF

MANKOFF

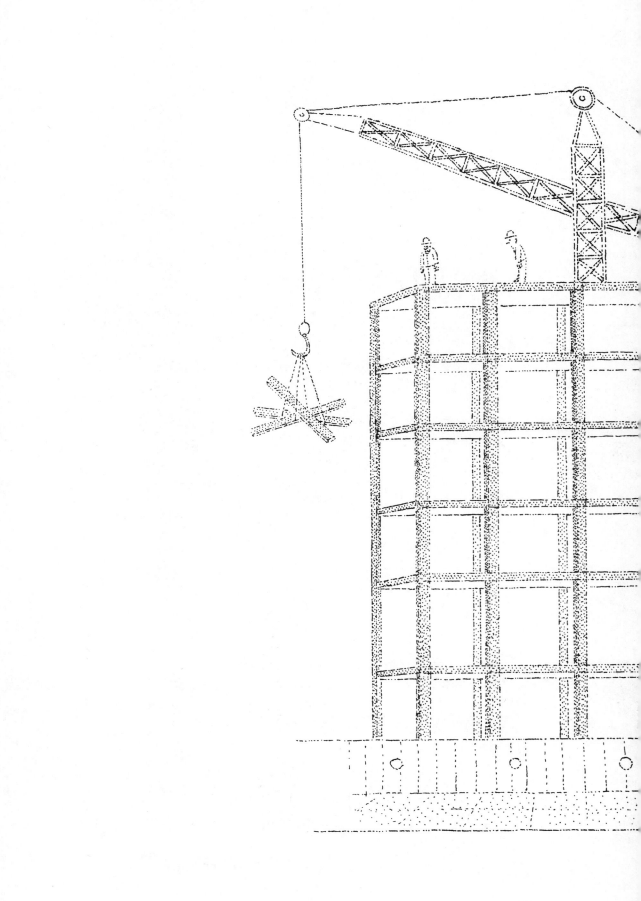

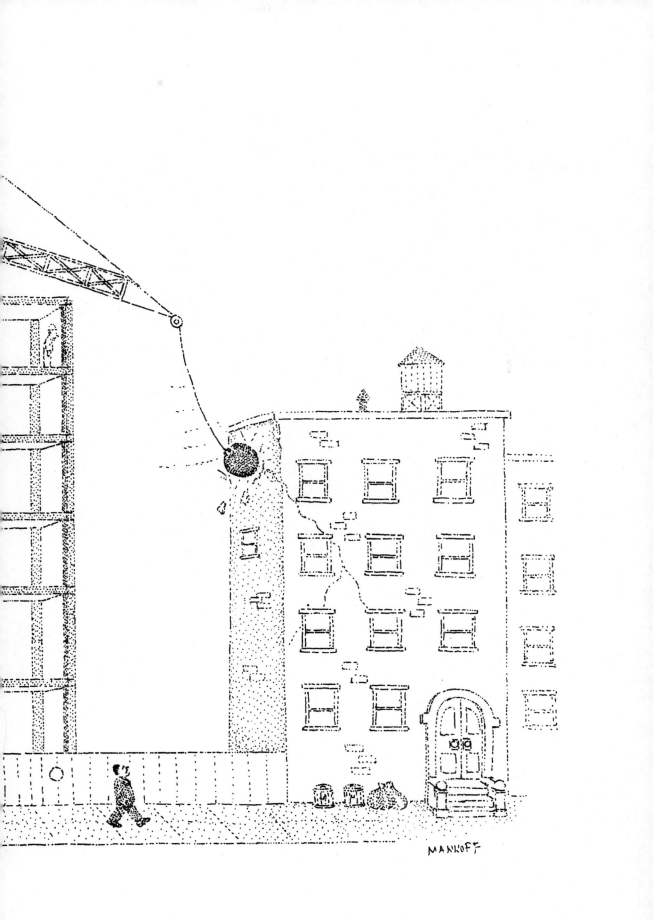

MANNOFF

Masters of Illusion
Igon Jastrow

"Igon Jastrow was, pound for pound, the greatest illusionist of his era (September 1923 to November of the same year). He is pictured above during his heyday (October 3, 1923), with his famous Jastrow illusion, in which figure B appears much larger than figure A although both figures are identical in every respect. Though Jastrow was a certified master of illusion audiences found it hard to accept his statement that both figures were identical. Even when he had this statement notarized they remained skeptical and often demanded refunds. In fact, Jastrow could not even convince his own wife that the figures were the same size and she divorced him when he continued to pester her about it. Ironically, Jastrow's wife won custody of the illusion while Jastrow got the children, who were identical twins. At least according to Jastrow they were identical; his wife always claimed that one was much larger."

Urban Hazards: The Garbage Storm

Periodic Table (c. 450 B.C.)

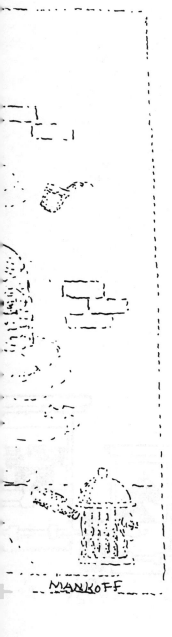

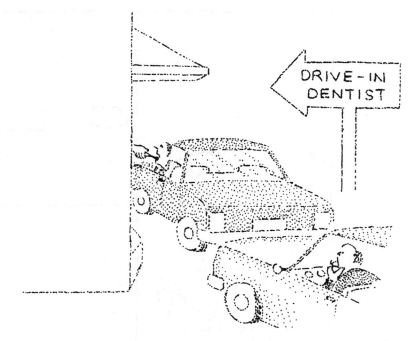

MANKOFF

"Simon says, 'Go to work, have a few martinis at lunch, come home, have a drink, eat, watch some T.V., and go to sleep.'"

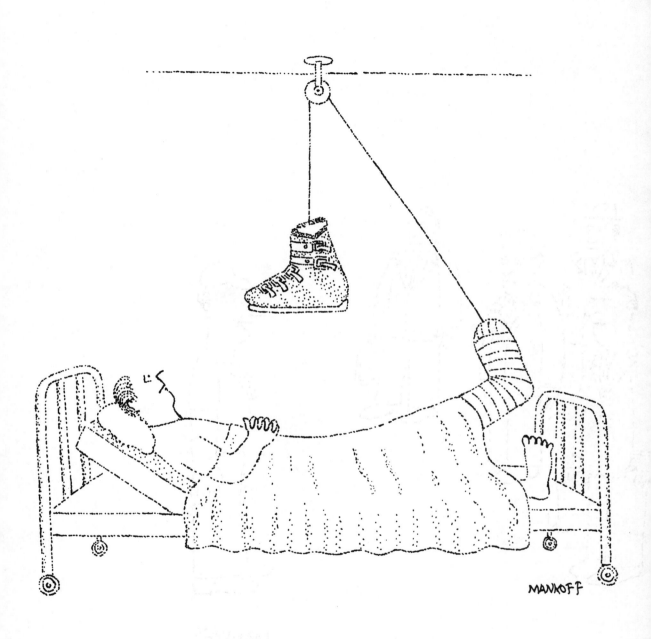

MANKOFF

"She's going to be another day, Mr. Houlihan. I told you when you brought her in that the boys had never worked on a Steinway before."

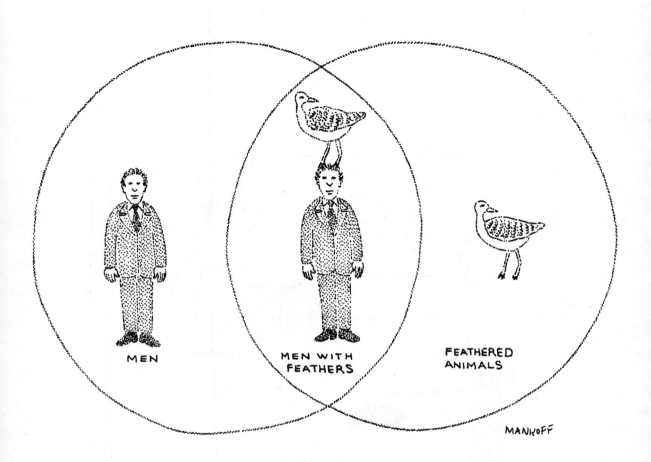

MEN

MEN WITH
FEATHERS

FEATHERED
ANIMALS

MANKOFF

"Dad, if a tree falls in the forest, and the media aren't there to cover it, has the tree really fallen?"

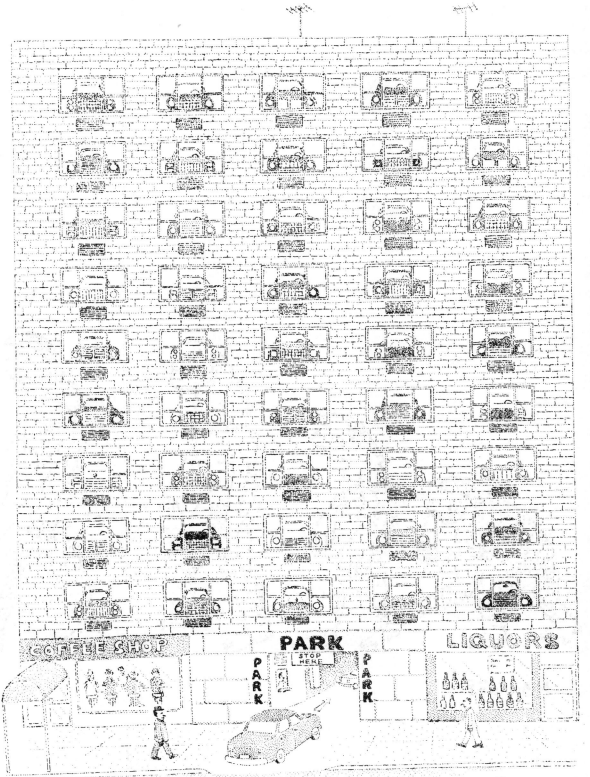

MANKOFF

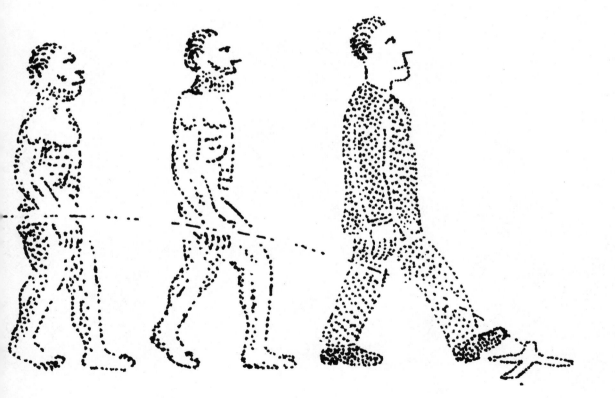

"All right, up against the wall, sexists!"

"O.K. guys, let's have a good clean fight. No racial epithets, ethnic slurs, or disparaging remarks about place of national origin. No derogation of religious persuasian, political affiliation, or sexual orientation. In case of a knockdown go immediately to a neutral corner and refrain from any taunts, jeers, or gibes about pugilistic ability."

Tour De Venice

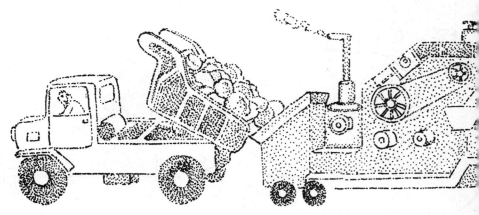

NANKOFF

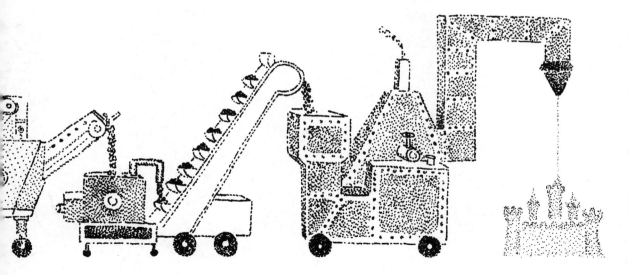

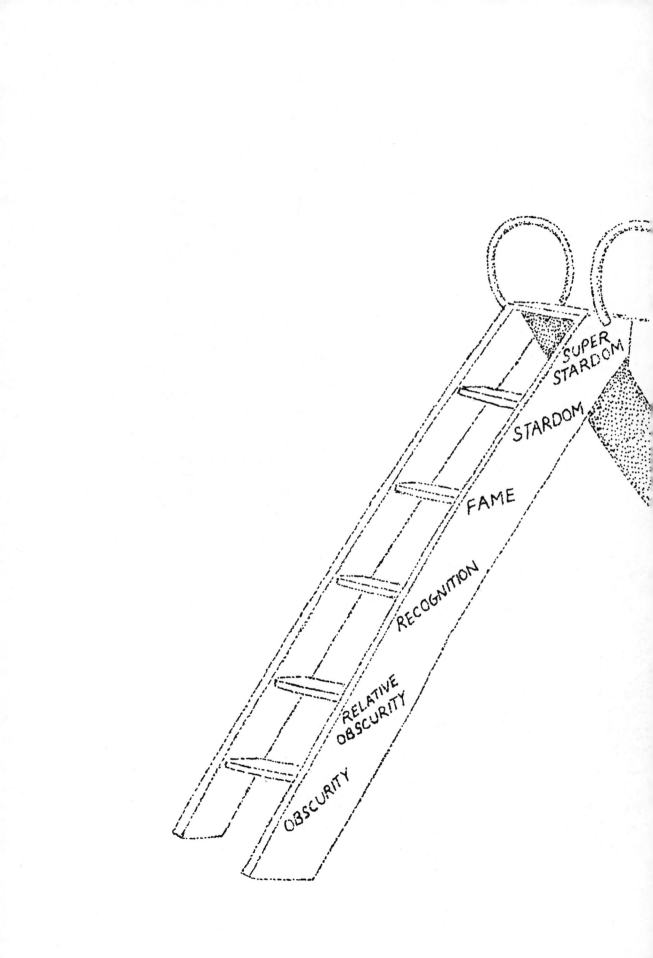

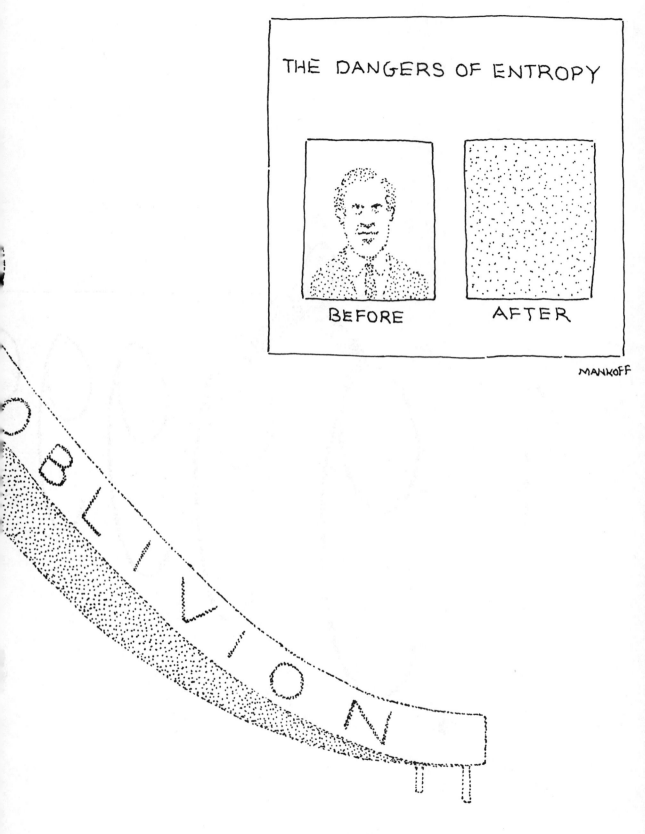

1. 1999

MANKOFF

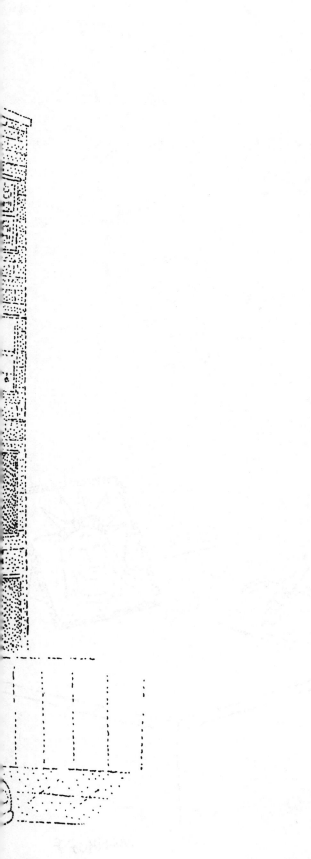

The three flying Romanos
plus investment counselor,
Arnold Wasserman (second from
the top).

MANKOFF

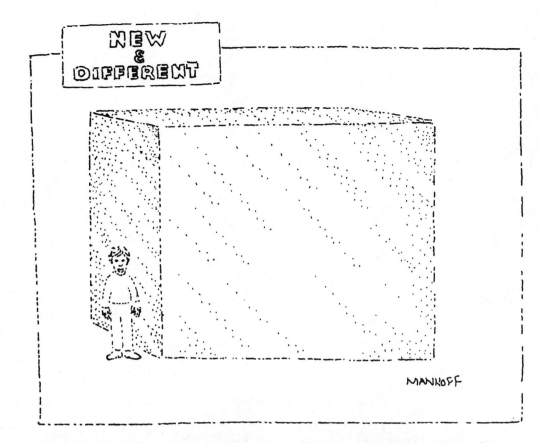

This two-hundred thousand pound steel cube represents a unique gift for children. In a day and age when fads in toys and trinkets appear and vanish almost before you turn around, here is a gift that won't be outgrown, broken, worn-out, lost or forgotten a month after Christmas. Under $2000.

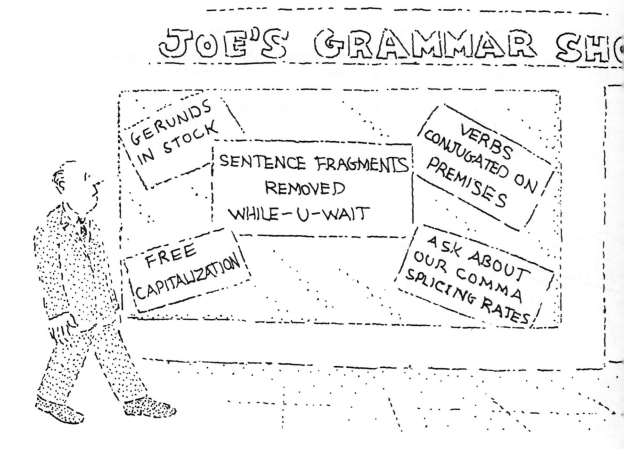

HOW TO DRAW A DOG

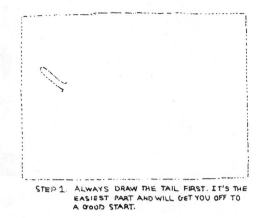

STEP 1. ALWAYS DRAW THE TAIL FIRST. IT'S THE EASIEST PART AND WILL GET YOU OFF TO A GOOD START.

STEP 2. NOW ADD THE PAWS. REMEMBER, THE DOG IS A QUADRAPED, SO YOU'LL NEED FOUR OF THEM.

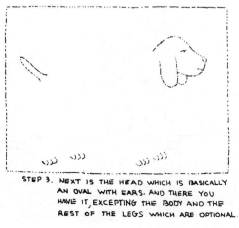

STEP 3. NEXT IS THE HEAD WHICH IS BASICALLY AN OVAL WITH EARS. AND THERE YOU HAVE IT, EXCEPTING THE BODY AND THE REST OF THE LEGS WHICH ARE OPTIONAL.

MANKOFF

MANKOFF

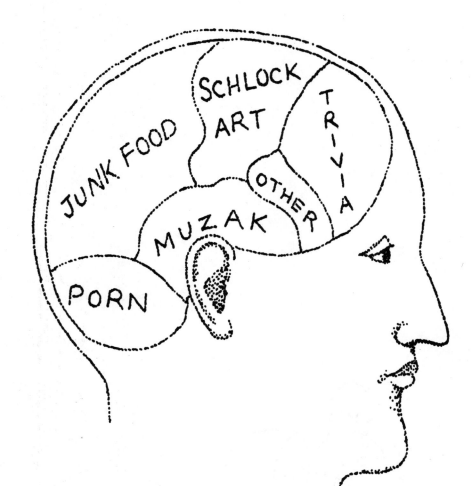

MANKOFF

Parapsychologist

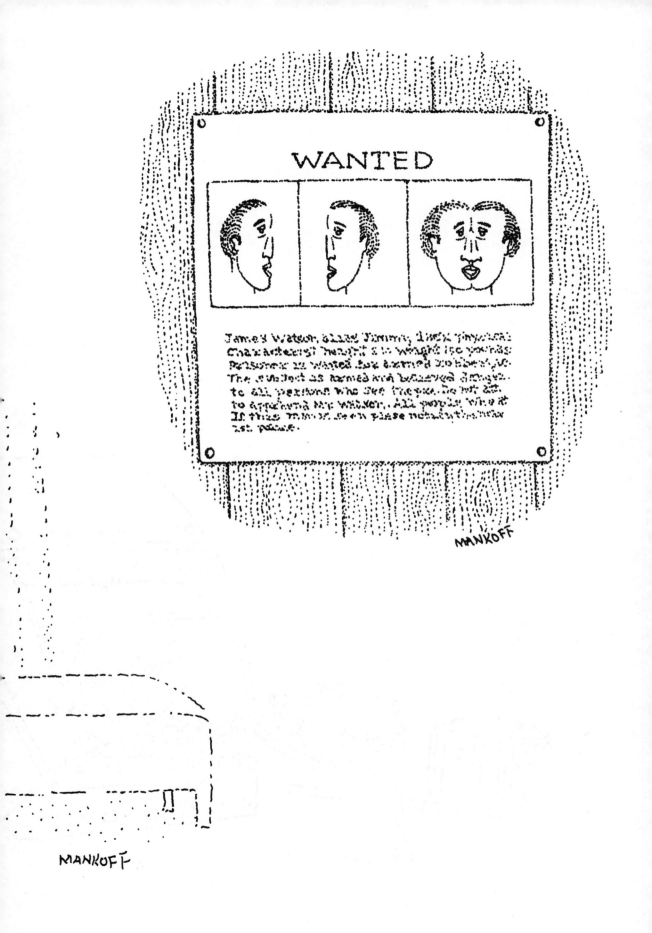

MANKOFF

MANKOFF

MANKOFF

Macho Vegetarian

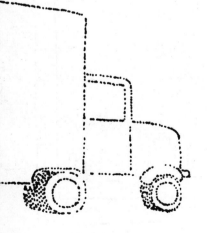

MANKOFF

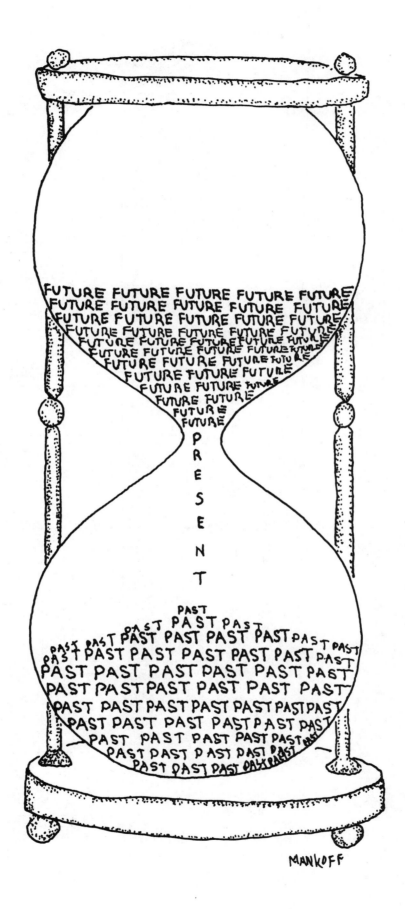

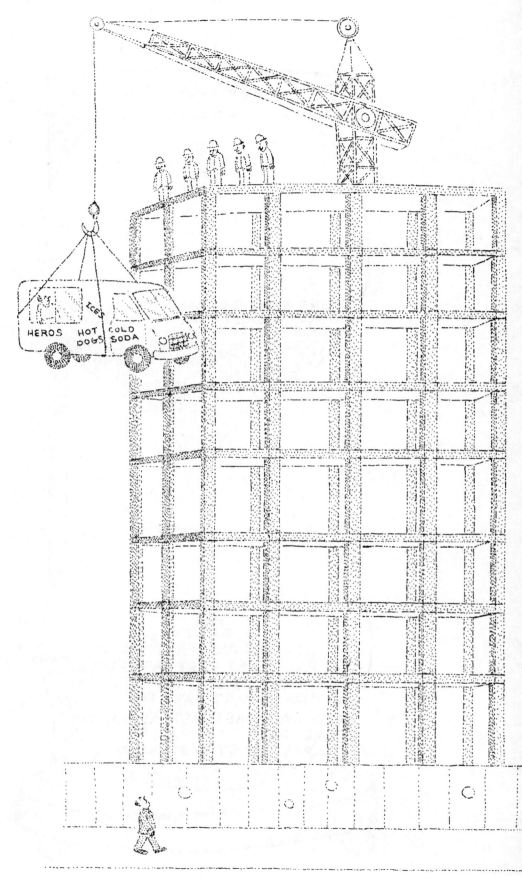

"Please tell the king I've remembered the punch line."

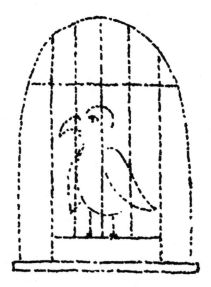

MANKOFF

MANKOFF

STUFF YOUR FACE

RESTAURANT

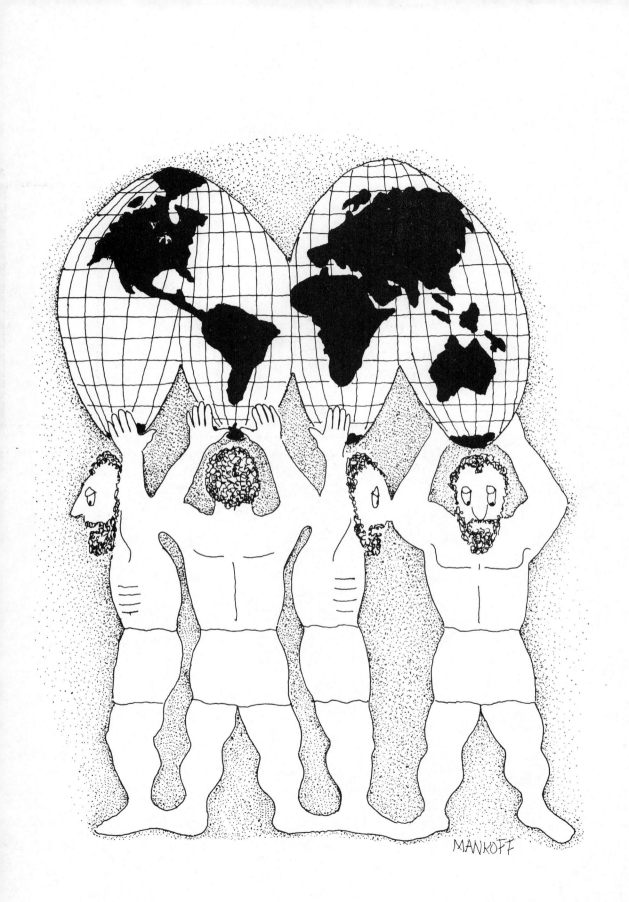

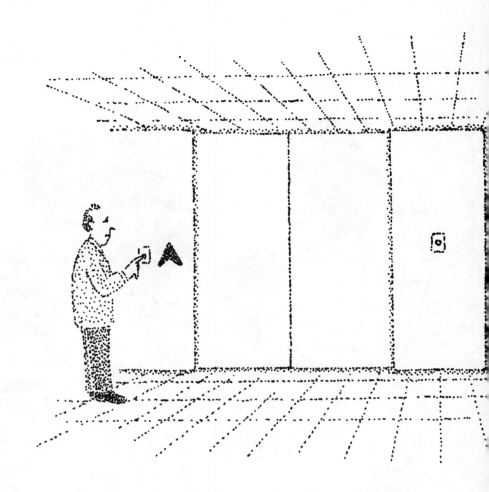

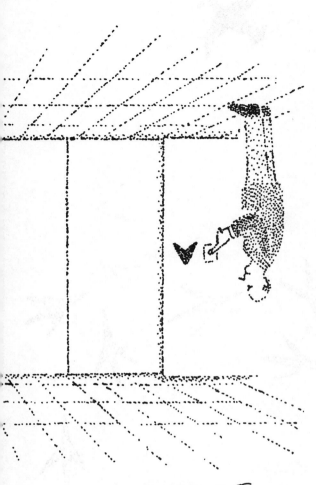

MANKOFF

MANKOFF

"*I think you two may hit it off. Craig, here, is an attractive male academic in his early forties who seeks a warm, vivacious woman delighting in conversation, arts, and nature for an evolving romantic commitment, possibly marriage, while you, Vivian, are a good-looking, intelligent, stimulating woman in her late thirties who seeks an educated, unattached, well-bred man concerned with ideas, culture, and the environment with whom to share your life interests and companionship.*"

"Of course, the mileage you get on the road will depend on how and where you drive and other varying factors, such as wind direction and velocity."

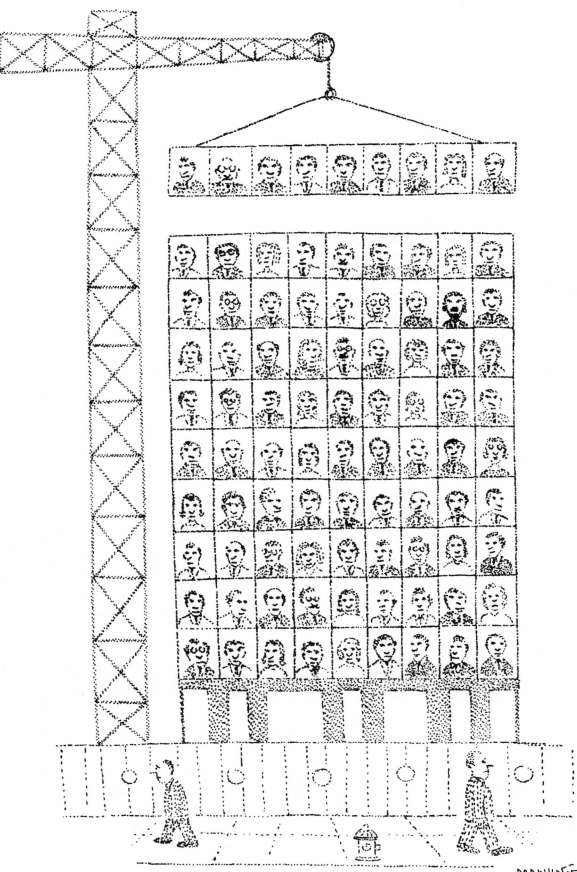

MANKOFF

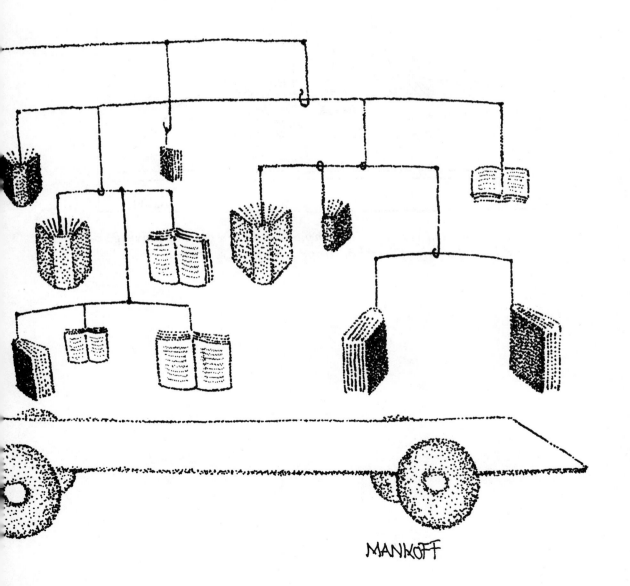

MANKOFF

"All you need is a bicycle pump, an ordinary deck of playing cards, and a pair of deerskin slippers, and you're ready to begin."

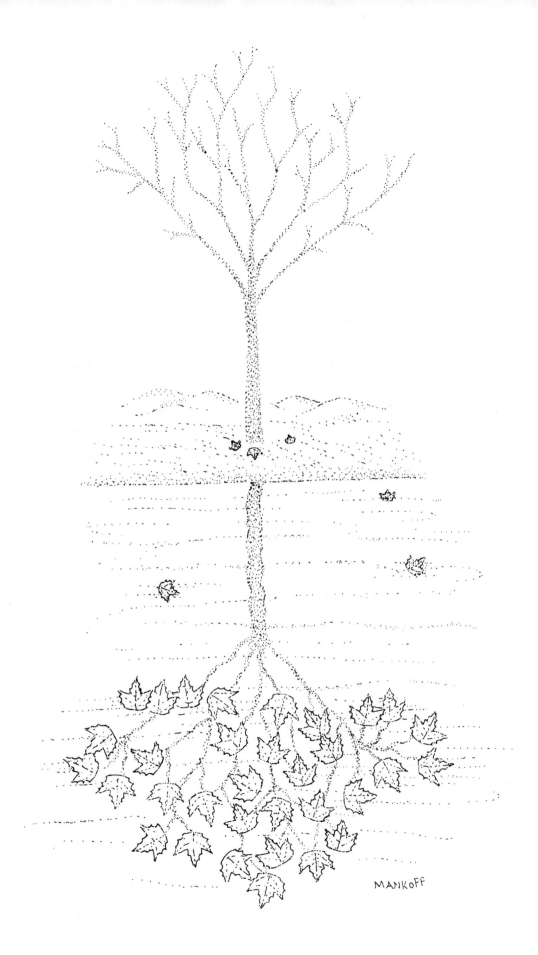

VETERANS
OF
FOREIGN FOOD

MANKOFF

"I'm sorry, but you'll have to go now. We're off after Labor Day."

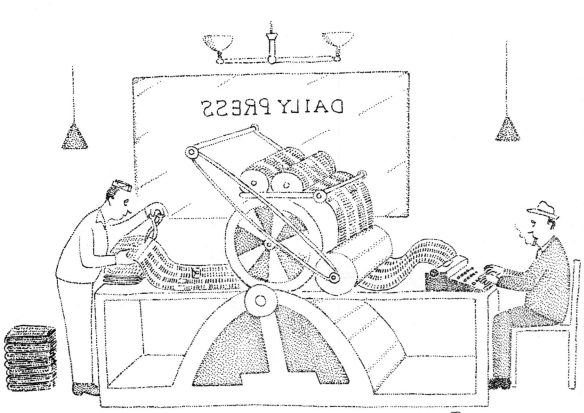

MANKOFF

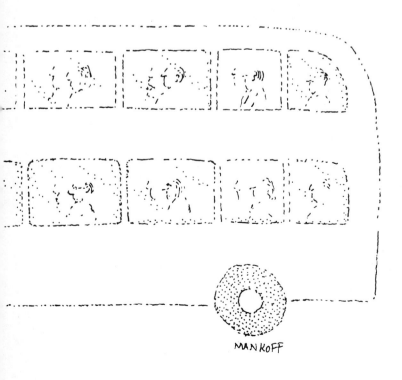

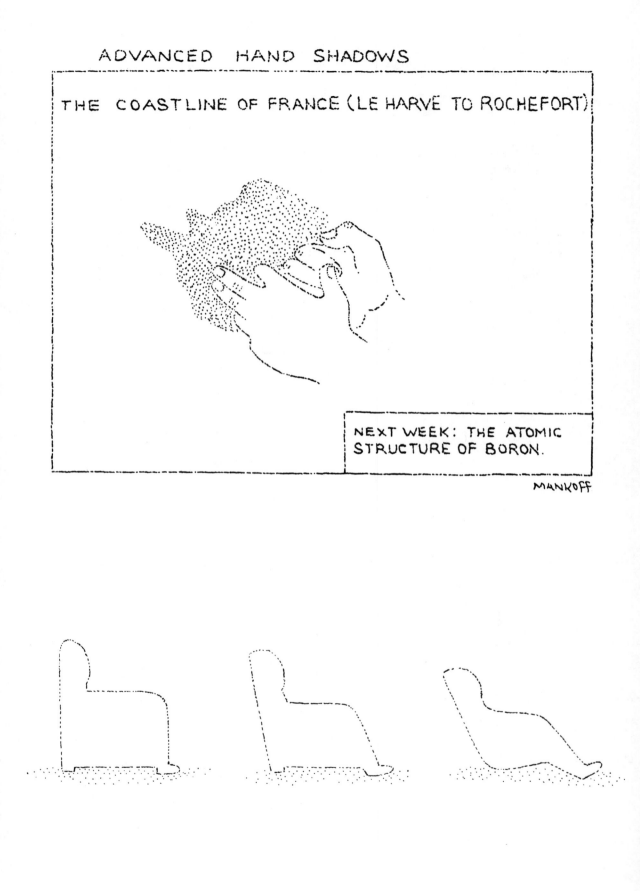

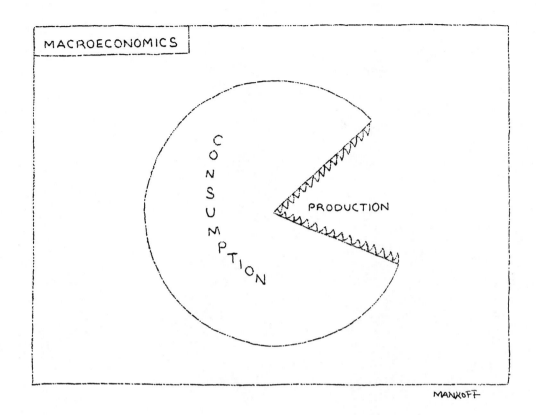

MACROECONOMICS

MANKOFF

MANKOFF

"I'd like you two to meet. Individually, neither one of you is very interesting, but together I'm hoping for a synergistic effect."

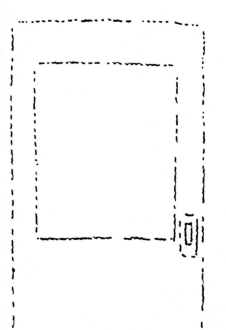

Thomas Kelly (a fictitious name) aged 42 (not his real age), in his home in Houston, where, actually, he does not live.

MANKOFF

Black's Knight passes GO and collects $200

The Tomb of the Unknown Quantity

"*Look, I know that 'less is more' and 'more is less', but 'enough is enough'.*"